THE
SHEPHERD BOY
OF BETHLEHEM

Told by
LUCY DIAMOND

Illustrated by
KENNETH INNS

Publishers: Wills & Hepworth Ltd., Loughborough

PRINTED IN ENGLAND

©

THE SHEPHERD BOY
OF BETHLEHEM

This is a story which begins in **Bethlehem** a long time ago—a thousand years before the little Lord Jesus was born there.

It is a story about David, who was the youngest of the eight sons of Jesse.

Jesse was one of the richest and best known men in Bethlehem. He was good and kind, and liked and respected by everyone.

Now he was old, his sons looked after the olive groves and vineyards which belonged to their father, and ploughed, and sowed, and reaped in his fields of barley.

4

The three eldest sons were strong stalwart men—good looking and brave, and when the kings of other tribes made war against the land of Israel, then the three brothers would join the army of Saul their King, and would follow him into battle.

David was the youngest of the eight brothers. He was still only a boy and his work was to look after his father's sheep.

This was no easy task. A shepherd's life in that land was a hard one. David often had to go far from home, and wander for miles on the hills around Bethlehem to find the fresh grass and water the sheep needed.

The countryside was sometimes parched and dry, with the streams dried up and the wells few and far between. There were no walls or hedges to keep the sheep safely penned in, and David had to watch carefully or some of the flock might wander and get lost. It was dangerous country too. There were deep gullies and dark clefts in the hillsides, into which a sheep could so easily fall. Wild beasts lurked in them— lions and bears, who stole out at times to try to snatch away one of the flock.

But David was strong and brave and, like every shepherd, he went prepared and well armed. Hanging from the leather belt of his tunic he carried his rod—a heavy club—and his shepherd's bag, and his sling, which he could use most skilfully.

If one of the sheep strayed from the flock David did not go after it. He fitted a stone to his sling and sent it with unerring aim to drop just beyond the wanderer. That frightened it, and sent the sheep hurrying back towards the shepherd to find safety in his care. To help him guide the flock, David carried a shepherd's staff with its crooked end.

So he sang—"The Lord is my shepherd. I shall not want. He maketh me to lie down in green pastures. He leadeth me beside the still waters. He restoreth my soul. He leadeth me in the paths of righteousness for His name's sake. Yea—though I walk through the valley of the shadow of death I will fear no evil, for thou art with me, thy rod and thy staff they comfort me."

That is the loveliest song David ever made. It is wonderful to think that today we can read and sing this beautiful "Shepherd's psalm" which David first sang so long ago out on the hills of Bethlehem.

. . . .

King Saul had been chosen by God and anointed by Samuel the prophet to be King of Israel. At first he was a good and wise ruler, but afterwards he grew proud and wilful, and disobeyed and displeased the Lord Jehovah.

So God said he should not be king much longer.

Samuel the prophet lived at Ramah. He was very sad when God's word came to him, for he loved Saul, and had hoped great things from him. Then God spoke to Samuel in Ramah:

"How long will you mourn for Saul? Fill your horn with oil and go to Jesse in Bethlehem. I have chosen a king from among his sons."

So Samuel obeyed, and he came to Bethlehem.

There he called the people together and they all made themselves ready for a sacrifice.

Afterwards Jesse made a feast for Samuel, and the prophet saw his sons. He looked on the eldest and thought, "Surely this is the Lord's anointed."

"No, Samuel," the Lord answered. "This is not he. You are only looking on his face. The Lord looks on the heart. This man does not please me."

So seven sons passed before the prophet —but still Samuel said: "The Lord has not chosen these."

"Are all your children here?" he asked Jesse at last.

"There is still the youngest," was the answer. "He is in the fields keeping the sheep.

And Samuel said to Jesse, "Send and fetch him, for we will not sit down until he comes."

So the father sent, and brought him in, and David the shepherd boy came and stood before the prophet of Israel. Now David was a beautiful boy and goodly to look upon.

Then the Lord said to Samuel, "Arise and anoint him, for this is he."

Then Samuel took the horn of oil and anointed David in the midst of his brothers, and the spirit of the Lord came mightily upon him from that day.

So Samuel left Bethlehem and went home to Ramah, and David went back to his sheep.

Now King Saul was ill—worried and miserable. His wilfulness and disobedience had driven out the spirit of God from his heart, and it seemed as if an evil spirit put into his mind all sorts of ugly thoughts.

Saul's servants did not know what to do. They wanted to help him, for when Saul was at his best they loved and honoured him. One of them at last thought of something.

"Let your servants seek out a man who is a skilful player upon the harp," he said to the unhappy king. "Let him play to you, and see if his music will soothe you and make you well again."

"Find a man who can play well, and bring him to me," Saul ordered.

Then one of the servants said, "I know where we can find one who will make sweet music. I have seen the son of Jesse the Bethlehemite who can play the harp wonderfully. He is brave and wise, and good to look at—and the Lord is with him."

So Saul sent messengers to Jesse saying "Send me David, the son who looks after your sheep."

Jesse took an ass laden with bread, and a skin of wine, and a kid, and sent these presents by his son David to Saul.

That is how the shepherd boy came to the palace of Saul the King.

Saul looked at this beautiful happy boy who stood before him, and he loved him greatly.

"Play to me," he said.

So David played upon his harp, and with the ripple of the music it seemed as if all the sweetness of the open air—the songs of the birds—the coolness of running water —had stolen into that darkened room. Saul was soothed and refreshed by the lovely melodies, and he soon began to feel much better. The evil thoughts were driven right away as David played. Saul was full of joy. He sent to Jesse saying, "Will you let your son stay with me for a while? I like him, and his music delights me."

So David stayed with Saul.

. . . . . .

Israel was at war. The Philistines had invaded their country and pitched their tents in the Vale of Elah, about twelve miles from Bethlehem.

When the Philistines encamped on one hillside, Saul gathered his army together and set it in battle order on the other hill. So the two armies faced each other across the valley.

Then there came out of the Philistines' camp a huge giant—Goliath of Gath. He was nearly ten feet tall, enormously broad and strong, and his face was terrible to look on ! He was dressed in heavy armour, with a helmet of brass on his head, and brass on his legs and shoulders. The giant carried a spear whose shaft was like a great beam, and his shield bearer went before him with his massive shield.

The huge Philistine stood and cried to the armies of Israel:

"Why have you set your battle in order? I am a Philistine, and you the servants of Saul. Choose a man and let him come down to me."

But all the men of Israel, when they saw this monster, fled from him and were terribly afraid. No one dared to think of fighting him.

For forty days this huge Philistine came down into the valley at morning and at eventide. Each time he shouted defiantly:

"Give me a man that we may fight together."

And for forty days no champion was found in all the army of Israel.

Now the three eldest sons of Jesse had gone after Saul to the battle, but David still kept his father's sheep in Bethlehem.

One day Jesse said to his youngest son, "Take some of this parched corn and these ten loaves, and carry them as quickly as you can to your brothers at the camp. You may take these ten cheeses to give to their captain. See how your brothers are getting on and bring me word."

So David got up very early in the morning, loaded an ass with the gifts, and set off across the hills on his journey to the Vale of Elah. He came to where the wagons made a barricade around the camp and, leaving the ass with the keeper of the baggage, he went to find his brothers.

David had only just begun to give them his father's message when there came a great shout from across the valley. The giant Philistine had come down to make his morning challenge.

Even Saul, who stood head and shoulders above any man in his army, dared not venture to face such a monster.

Some men who were standing by said to David: "Have you seen the huge giant who is challenging the men of Israel? He is terrible. Everyone is afraid of him."

"If anyone can fight and kill him the King will give him great riches, and let him marry his own daughter."

"Is it not shameful that everyone is afraid?" David asked. "Who is this Philistine who dares to defy the armies of the living God?"

Eliab, David's eldest brother, heard these words and was very angry and he rebuked him saying, "Who is looking after our father's sheep? I know your naughtiness! You have only come here to get a chance of watching the battle."

Eliab had not yet seen the gifts Jesse had sent for his sons, and so David felt rather hurt.

"What have I done wrong?" he asked. "Isn't there need for someone to say what is true—that the Lord Jehovah will fight for his people."

Then a soldier ran and told the King what David was saying in the camp.

"Bring this man to me." Saul ordered.

So David was brought before the King.

Saul was surprised when David said, "Don't let anyone be afraid because of this Philistine. I will go and fight him."

"You! You cannot go!" Saul said at once. "You are only a boy and this giant has been a skilled fighter from his youth."

"I can fight," David answered. "I keep my father's sheep, and when a lion or a bear came out and took a lamb from the flock, I went after him. I took the lamb from the lion's mouth. I caught him by his beard, and smote him and killed him. I killed the bear too!"

"The Lord saved me from the lion and the bear. He will fight for me against this Philistine who defies the armies of the living God."

Saul listened to these brave words.

"Very well," he said at last. "Go, and the Lord Jehovah shall be with you."

"But if you are going to fight such a monster as this giant whom our strongest men fear, you will need to be well prepared. You must go to meet him armed like a soldier."

Then the King had his own armour brought for David. He put a helmet of brass on his head to keep off the giant's blows. He dressed him in a coat of mail, and gave him a sword to fasten at his belt. But when David tried to move, the heavy, clanking armour weighed him down, and he could not draw the sword from its sheath.

" I cannot go with these," he said to Saul. " I am not used to them. I have never tried to fight with a sword."

So David laid aside the shining armour, and stood there in his shepherd's dress with his rod and his sling at his belt. He took his staff in his hand and went out from Saul.

He went out to fight the giant Goliath with the weapons which he used day by day to defend his sheep.

But he went to face this terrible foe with a prayer in his heart—trusting in the Lord Jehovah.

David chose five smooth stones from the brook, and put them in the shepherd's bag at his belt. Then with his sling in his hand he went down the hillside to meet the Philistine.

The news spread like wildfire through the camp that David the shepherd boy was going out to fight the giant. All the army of Israel ran together to watch.

A huge glittering figure came striding down the other hill, as Goliath advanced to meet the man who was brave enough to dare to answer his challenge. His shield-bearer walked before him and, with his enormous spear and his great sword, the giant was a fearsome sight!

Now when this mighty Philistine saw a slim boy coming towards him, he laughed scornfully. Then he was angry!

"Who do they think that I am," he raged, "that they send a boy with a staff to beat me!"

"Come to me," he shouted to David, "I will soon make an end of you, and leave you for wild beasts to eat!"

Then David said to the Philistine: "You come to me in armour with a sword and a spear—but I come to you in the name of the Lord of Hosts—the God of the armies of Israel whom you have defied! The Lord will fight for me today! I will kill you, and everyone shall know that there is a God in Israel."

Furiously the Philistine came near to meet this daring boy, and David hurried and ran forward to meet his foe. He put his hand in his bag and took out a stone. He fitted it into his sling, and then, with unerring skill, he slung it—aiming at the one spot not protected by the giant's armour.

Swiftly the stone sped through the air—and sank deep into Goliath's forehead!

He fell on his face to the earth!

In an instant David was upon him and, drawing the giant's own sword from its sheath, he cut off Goliath's head.

A mighty shout went up from the armies of Israel—but when the Philistines saw that their champion was dead, they turned and ran away terrified and dismayed.

Then Saul's army rushed across the valley, captured all the tents and armour of their enemies, and pursued the frightened Philistines until they were far beyond the borders of their own country.

David was brought in triumph to Jerusalem, and all the people cheered and rejoiced, and delighted to do him honour.

That was the end of David's life as a shepherd in Bethlehem. Saul set him over the men in his army, and kept him in his own household, while Jonathan, the King's son became his devoted friend and loved him dearly.

All this did not spoil the young hero, who had trusted in God to save him from the giant. We are told that " David behaved himself wisely, and the Lord was with him."

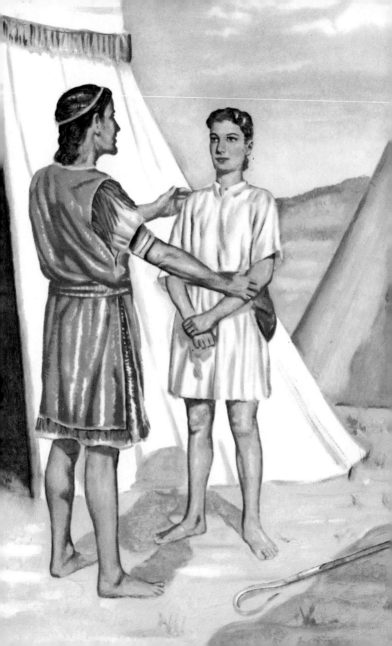

Series 522